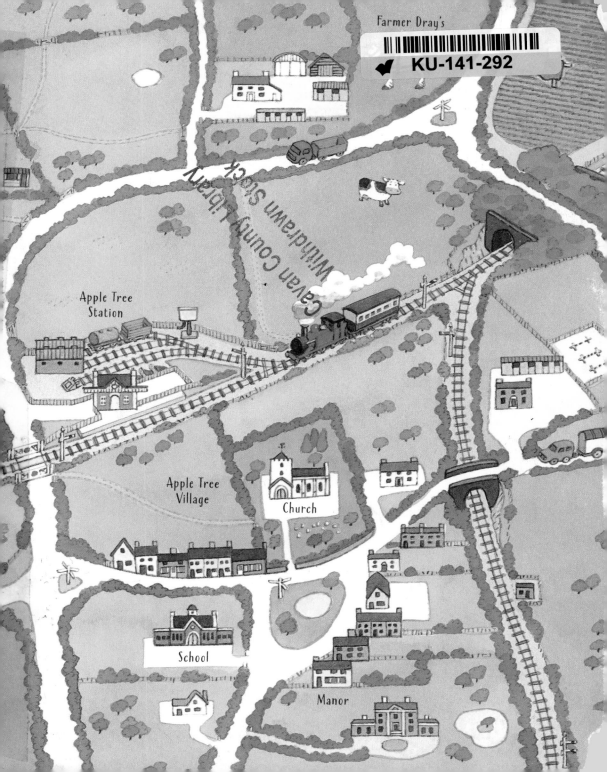

Farmer Dray's

Apple Tree
Station

Apple Tree
Village

Church

School

Manor

Usborne Farmyard Tales

Poppy and Sam's
Bedtime Stories

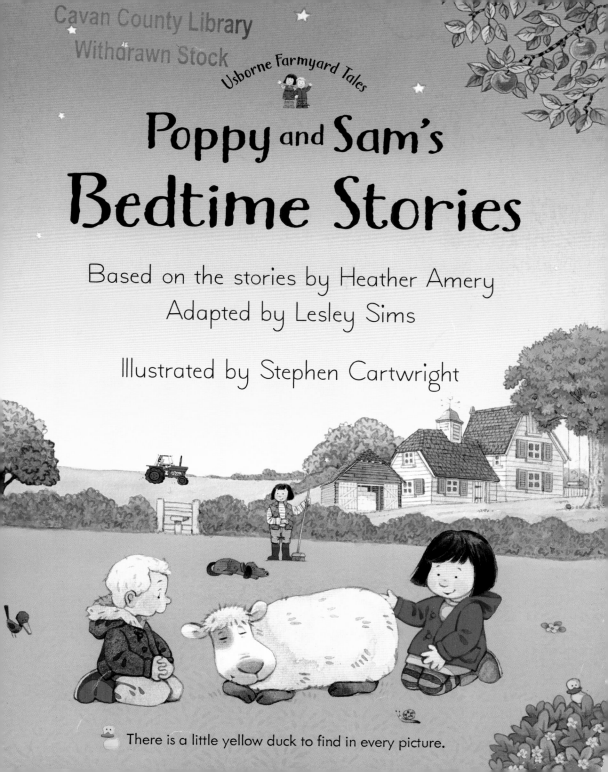

Usborne Farmyard Tales

Poppy and Sam's
Bedtime Stories

Based on the stories by Heather Amery
Adapted by Lesley Sims

Illustrated by Stephen Cartwright

There is a little yellow duck to find in every picture.

Contents

Welcome to Apple Tree Farm

Poppy and Sam Boot live on Apple Tree Farm. Here they are, with some of the characters you'll meet in their adventures.

Poppy

Sam

Rusty the dog

Whiskers the cat

Mr. and Mrs. Boot

Ted, who helps on the farm

Daisy the cow

Woolly the sheep

Fluff the kitten

Mr. Bran
the delivery man

Henry
the handyman

Farmer Dray and his
carthorse, Dolly

Mr. Straw
the scarecrow

Kitten's Day Out

It was delivery day at Apple Tree Farm.
Mr. Bran had arrived with sacks
of food for the cows.

Mrs. Boot and Ted were helping to unload
the truck.

Sam was playing with Fluff the kitten.
"Keep her out of the way, Sam," said Ted.

Mr. Bran drove away, with a 'Beep! Beep!'
"Goodbye!" called Poppy and Ted.

"Where's Fluff?" asked Sam.

Ted looked around the barn. "She's not in here," he said.

"I can't see her anywhere," said Poppy. "I even looked over in the cowshed."

"Maybe she jumped into Mr. Bran's truck when we weren't looking," Mrs. Boot suggested. "Take my car, Ted, and see if you can find them."

"Everyone into the car," said Ted. "The Great Kitten Chase is on!"

After a while, they reached a crossroads. The question was, which way had Mr. Bran gone?

Is that his truck, up ahead?

15

Ted drove around two bends and down
a steep hill... into a massive puddle.

Splash! Water filled the engine.
The car spluttered and stopped.

"Everyone out!" said Ted. "I'll have to push us out of the puddle. It may take some time."

"We'll never find Mr. Bran now," said Sam.

Ted refused to give up. He started the car, and off they went again... to find a large flock of sheep wandering about in the road.

Ted honked the horn and, finally, the sheep ambled back to their field.

Honk!

Honk!

Honk!

They were driving along once more, when Sam
and Poppy shouted, "STOP!"
Ted slammed on the brakes.

"There's a truck in that farmyard," said Poppy.
"It might be Mr. Bran's."

"I know it's Mr. Bran's truck!" said Sam,
so Ted reversed the car back to the farm.

But it wasn't Mr. Bran's truck at all.

By now, it was getting late. "I'm afraid we'll have to head home," said Ted.

"We'll never find poor Fluff," Sam sighed.
"I'm sure we will," said Poppy, trying to cheer him up.

When they arrived home at Apple Tree Farm,
there was a surprise waiting for Sam.

"Fluff!" he cried.

Mr. Bran had brought her back. "Here you are, Sam," he said. "Don't worry. She's fine."

Sam smiled and hugged his kitten. "Did you enjoy your day out with Mr. Bran?" he said. "You must be very tired. I think it's time for supper and bed."

"And not just for the kitten," said Mrs. Boot, with a smile. "You've all had an adventure today!"

The Old Steam Train

Poppy and Sam were playing Chase
with Rusty.

"He's so fast!" panted Sam.

Poppy laughed. "He's too fast for me."

"Poppy! Sam!" Mrs. Boot called.
"Come inside and put your coats on.
We're going on a trip."

"Where are we going?" asked Poppy.

"It's a surprise," said Mrs. Boot, as she helped Sam to put on his coat.

Dad is there already!

They walked down the lane, full of questions.
"Are we going to the fair?" asked Poppy.
"Is it a show?" asked Sam.

Are we nearly there yet?

They soon arrived...
"It's the old train station!" said Sam.

"But why is it so busy?" asked Poppy. "Why is everyone cleaning it? There aren't any trains."

Mrs. Boot just smiled.

"Hello," said their friend, Henry the handyman.

"Have you come to lend a hand?"

Poppy and Sam set to work, helping Henry paint the station.

"Here you are," said Sam, passing up a can of paint.

"Could you help me, Poppy?" asked Mrs. Boot.

Poppy was sweeping
the platform when there
was a 'Choo! Choo!'

Choo!
Choo!

"Look!" she cried. "It's a steam train."
"That's a lot of smoke!" said Sam.

With a 'chuggity-chug, chuggity-chug', the train puffed into the platform and came to a stop.

It gave a 'Toot! Toot!' and all the helpers waved and cheered.

"That's Dad!" said Sam, as he looked
in the cab. "What's he
doing there?"

"Dad's helping to drive the train," said Mrs. Boot.
"Lucky Dad," said Sam.

"And you can go for a ride," Mrs. Boot told them, opening the door. "Take Rusty with you."

"You wait there," said Mrs. Boot. "I'll be back
in a minute. I have one more surprise for you!"

Mrs. Boot disappeared and returned a moment later... wearing a jacket and cap. "I'm the train conductor!" she said. "Just for today."

"All aboard," she shouted, waving a green flag. Then she jumped on the train herself and closed the door, still waving the flag.

The train let out another 'Toot! Toot!'
Clouds of smoke puffed out of its chimney
and they set off down the track.

They watched the old station slowly go past
the window.

"You can see the new paint!" said Sam.

"It looks good," said Mrs. Boot.

"That was a fun surprise," said Poppy. "I love steam trains."

Mrs. Boot smiled. "And now that the old station is open again," she said, "we can ride on the steam train every weekend!"

"Hurray!" said Poppy and Sam.

The Scarecrow's Secret

One bright spring day, Poppy and Sam were helping Mrs. Boot on the farm.

"Look at all these eggs we've collected," said Poppy, showing her the basket.

"And we only dropped one," said Sam.
"That's wonderful!" said Mrs. Boot. "Now can you help Daddy?"

They found Mr. Boot working in the barn.
He seemed to be tying straw to a pole.

"What are you doing, Dad?" asked Sam.
"Are you making something for the farm?"

"I am," said Mr. Boot, putting a sack over one end of the pole. "I wonder if you'll guess what it is. It's not finished yet."

"First, I'll need my old coat from the shed. Please can you get it? Bring one of my old hats, too, and a scarf and gloves."

When they came back, Dad had drawn a face on the sack.

"I know, I know!" Sam cried. "It's a scarecrow!"

"It is indeed," said Mr. Boot.

"He looks good in your old coat, Dad!" said Poppy.

With a scarf and hat, the scarecrow was almost dressed.

"Don't forget his gloves," said Sam.

What can we call him?

Mr. Straw!

"It's time to get Mr. Straw to the cornfield," said Mr. Boot. "Poppy, you help carry him. Sam, you can bring the shovel."

In the middle of the cornfield, Mr. Boot dug a big hole. Then he heaved Mr. Straw into it.

Sam helped to fill in the hole, so Mr. Straw stayed standing up.

"He does look real," said Poppy. She grinned.
"I bet he'll scare off all the crows!"

The next day, they went back to see how their scarecrow was doing.

There wasn't a single bird in the cornfield. "Great job, Mr. Straw!" said Mr. Boot.

They went for a walk and saw another
scarecrow in a nearby field.

Birds were eagerly gobbling up all the corn.
They were even standing on the scarecrow.

"Mr. Straw is the best scarecrow ever," Sam said proudly, a few days later. "He looks alive."

"He really does," said Poppy, in surprise. "Look! His coat seems to be moving up and down."

"That's very strange," she added. "How is his coat moving? Let's go and see."

"Let's creep up quietly," said Sam, and they tiptoed across the field.

Mr. Straw's coat was definitely twitching.
Then it let out a funny noise.

Puzzled, Poppy and Sam gently opened the scarecrow's coat to find...

Whiskers!

There was their cat, Whiskers, with two little kittens, nestled in the straw.

"So that's how Mr. Straw scared away all the birds!" said Poppy. "He was hiding Whiskers. What a secret!"

Camping Out

"Who's this?" asked Sam, one afternoon,
as a car pulled up outside Apple Tree Farm.

"I've no idea," said Mrs. Boot.

A friendly-looking family got out. The man gave
a cheerful wave.

"We're the Cole family and we're looking for somewhere to camp," said the man. "May we camp on your farm?"

71

"Of course!" said Mrs. Boot, and she called Mr. Boot to show them the way to a field.

"Follow us!" called Mr. Boot.
"Yes, this way!" said Sam.

"What a peaceful place," said Mrs. Cole,
as Poppy helped her unload the car. "We'll have
a lovely week, staying here."

In no time at all, Mr. Cole had put up the tent. It looked like a little house. Rusty was so interested, he didn't even notice the rabbits.

"Do you think your mother could give us some milk, and some water?" Mrs. Cole asked.

"Of course!" said Poppy.

At the farmhouse, Mrs. Boot found water
and a jug of creamy milk.

"And would you like some freshly-laid eggs?"
asked Poppy.

"We collected them this morning," said Sam.

The Coles were delighted, and headed back
to their camp to cook supper.

"I'd like to go camping,"
said Poppy.

Can we?
Please?

"It's a warm evening," said Mr. Boot. "Let's go
and find your tent."

The tent was tricky to put together — even with Sam and Rusty trying to help.

At last, their little blue tent was up. Poppy was thrilled. She wanted to go in right away, but Mrs. Boot had other ideas.

Supper and teeth brushing first!

As soon as they had finished supper, brushed their teeth and were ready for bed, Poppy and Sam raced to the tent.

Inside, the tent was snug. Poppy and Sam
climbed into their sleeping bags.
   "I'm too excited to sleep!" said Poppy.

   "Me too!" Sam agreed. "And-" He stopped.
There was a strange sound right outside the tent.

Poppy and Sam looked at each other.
It sounded as if something BIG was out there.

Poppy took a deep breath and peered through the tent flaps.

Daisy the cow had come to say hello.

Daisy poked her enormous head into the tent. "Moooo!" she said.

Daisy! You naughty cow. Get out!

The next thing they knew, Daisy had run off...
taking the tent with her!

"Hey!" cried Sam. "Come back with our tent."
"We'll have to go home," sighed Poppy.

"Whatever is going on?" asked Mr. Boot, coming to the farmhouse door.

Dad, Daisy stole our tent!

"Oh dear," he said, at the news about Daisy. "Maybe Daisy wanted to try camping, too!"

"Never mind," he added. "Come inside.
We can make a tent under the kitchen table."
"That sounds fun," said Sam, with a yawn.

"Can we do that tomorrow?" asked Poppy.
"Tonight, I'd like my own comfy bed!"

Surprise Visitors

Poppy and Sam were finishing their breakfast
when they heard loud noises coming from outside.

Is that the
cows?

"It sounds like the cows," Mrs. Boot said, looking worried. "And they seem upset."

The three of them rushed to the
field to investigate. The poor cows
were running away.

A huge hot-air balloon was floating right over
their field. "Wow!" said Sam.

The balloon drifted down and the basket landed on the grass with a bump.

Two people inside the basket waved. "Hello," they called out.

"I'm Alice and this is Tim," the woman said to Mrs. Boot. "Is this your field? I'm so sorry we scared your cows."

"We ran out of gas," Tim explained.

"We never know where we will land, so our friend follows us in his truck," said Alice.

There was a 'Beep! Beep!' and then a man called out, "Hello!"

"Here he is, now," she added.

The truck had rolled up with two new gas cylinders for the balloon.

"You arrived in perfect time!" said Alice, as she helped unload the cylinders.

Tim took the empty cylinders from the basket and loaded it up with the new ones.

"We'll be on our way again soon," he promised. "And then your cows can have some peace! Do you want to help me?" he asked Poppy and Sam.

"We need to fill the balloon with hot air again before we take off," Tim told them.

Tim and his friend took a large fan from the truck and set it up in front of the balloon.

Poppy and Sam helped to hold the balloon open. The fan was switched on and the balloon filled with air.

It grew bigger... and bigger... and bigger!

"Poppy and Sam have been so helpful, I think they deserve a ride," said Alice.

"What a good idea!" said Tim. "You can come too," he added to Mrs. Boot.

"Oh, please let's go," Poppy begged.

"Tim will only fly a little way," said Alice.
"And the truck can bring you all back."

"Thank you," said Mrs. Boot, climbing into the basket. "It does sound exciting."

Poppy clambered aboard too.

Alice swung Sam up and passed him to Tim. "Have fun!" she said.

Tim lit the gas burner
and the flames flared up
with a 'WHOOSH!'

Isn't it
loud!

Slowly, the balloon rose from the ground.
"Bye, Rusty!" called Sam. "See you later."

They floated high into the sky, blown along by the wind.

"Look! There's our farm," said Sam.

"And there's the truck," said Poppy.

"Everything looks tiny," Sam said. "Like toys!"

"Time to land," announced Tim, and the balloon floated gently back to the ground.

They landed in a field. Alice and the truck were there to meet them — and Rusty had come too.

"Thank you for an amazing trip!" Mrs. Boot shouted out, as the balloon took off again, with Alice and Tim inside.

Goodbye!

"What an adventure!" said Sam. "I'm going to dream about flying a hot-air balloon tonight!"

Market Day

"Hurray for market day!" sang Poppy, one morning. She and Sam were helping Mrs. Boot to get ready for a trip to the market.

I love going to the market!

Whenever they went, there was something new to see.

Mrs. Boot hitched the trailer to the back of her car. "Almost done," she said.

Soon, they were ready to go.

The market was full of noisy animals. Poppy, Sam and Mrs. Boot strolled past pens with pigs, sheep and cows.

"I like the cows best," said Sam.

Mooo!

"I want some geese," said Mrs. Boot.
"Let's go and look at the birds."

"I'd like four white geese," said Mrs. Boot.
She looked closely in all the cages.

"Those four look friendly," she said.
"They'll be perfect. I'll buy them."

Sam spotted two fluffy ducklings and showed them to Poppy.

Aren't they sweet!

"Oh, look," said Poppy, a moment later.
"There's a lonely duck. She looks sad."

Poor little duck.

"I wish I could buy her," thought Poppy.
Just then, Mrs. Boot called them to help her
collect a crate from the car.

Poppy opened the lid, while the lady selling the geese took them from their cage, one by one.

"You're coming to live at Apple Tree Farm!" Sam told them.

Carefully, Mrs. Boot lowered the geese into the crate.

Mrs. Boot had turned away to pay for the
geese, when one of them gave a loud 'Honk!'
and flew out of the crate.

"After it!" cried Sam. He and Poppy chased after the goose. It waddled up to a car with an open door, and...

...jumped inside!

"Now we've got it," said Sam, as Mrs. Boot and Poppy caught up with him.

But before they could rescue the goose, the car owner opened her door. Out flapped the goose. With a 'Honk!' it was off again.

The goose ran into the plant tent, skidding past
flower pots and sending them flying.
"Stop that goose!" panted Mrs. Boot.

A man on the flower stall sprang into action
as the goose flew over his head. "Leave it to me!"
he cried, and ran through his flowers to grab it.

Finally, the runaway goose was safely back in the crate.

"Time to go home," said Mrs. Boot.

"Please will you come and see a duck before we go?" asked Poppy. "I'd really like to buy it."

Please!

"I can use my birthday money," she added.

They went back to the birds and Poppy pointed out the duck.

"She is sweet," said Mrs. Boot.

Poppy counted out her money. "She's going to have lots of friends at Apple Tree Farm!" Poppy said, with a smile. "Then she won't be lonely any more."

Mrs. Boot picked up the crate of geese.
"Now it really is time to go
home!" she said.

"We have four friendly geese," said Sam.

"And I have my very own duck!" said Poppy.
"Markets are great."

The Runaway Tractor

"I love this time of year!" said Poppy, one day.
"Raking up the leaves is fun." She had made a
huge pile of rustling red and golden brown leaves.

"Playing with them is fun, too," said Sam, throwing a handful of leaves into the air. They danced on the breeze.

Morning, Poppy and Sam!

Ted waved, as he chugged by on his tractor. "I'm off to feed the sheep," he said.

Once the leaves had been swept up, Poppy and Sam went to play in the barn. All of a sudden, Sam thought he heard someone shouting.

He and Poppy raced outside. Ted was shouting in panic. The tractor was jolting down the hill, getting faster and faster.

"It's out of control," Ted shouted. "I can't stop it!"

The tractor went over a bump and the trailer came undone. It sped down the hill, smashing into the fence at the bottom.

CRASH!

The trailer tipped up and all the hay bales came tumbling out.

Meanwhile, poor Ted was doing his best to steer the tractor but it crashed through the fence and landed smack in the middle of the pond.

SPLASH!

The engine spluttered, let out a loud 'hisssssssss' and was silent.

Poppy and Sam ran to the pond. "Ted!
Are you all right?" they shouted together.
   Ted looked shaken. Slowly, he climbed
down from the tractor and waded out
of the pond.

"Your feet are soaked!" said Sam, as Ted
emptied pond water from his boots.

"What can we do to help?" asked Poppy.
"We'll need to get the tractor out of the pond,"
said Ted. He paused to think.

"This is a job for Farmer Dray," Ted said, squeezing pond water from his socks. "Will you go and call him?"

We'll be as quick as we can!

"Tell him we'll need Dolly," Ted called after them. "And plenty of rope!"

Farmer Dray was happy to help. He collected some rope and led Dolly, his carthorse, to the pond. "It's a good thing Ted wasn't hurt," he said.

"The tractor landed with a huge splash," Poppy told him. "It frightened all the ducks!"

Farmer Dray had brought two thick, sturdy
ropes with him. Ted tied one end to the tractor...

...while Farmer Dray tied the other end of the ropes to Dolly's harness. "Good girl," he said.

Ted got behind the tractor.
"One... two... three!" shouted Poppy and Sam.

GO! Push, Ted!
Pull, Dolly!

Ted began to push as Dolly began to heave on the tractor.

At first, nothing happened. Then, very, very slowly, the tractor began to roll out of the pond.

The tractor picked up speed. Ted slipped in the pond mud and fell flat on his face.

Arrgh!

Poor Ted was not having a good day.

"The tractor should be fine," said Farmer Dray, as soon as it was out of the pond. "The engine just needs to dry off."

Ted squelched out of the pond.
"So do I!" he said.

"Can I give you a lift to the farmhouse?"
Farmer Dray asked Poppy and Sam. He hoisted
them onto Dolly and climbed up behind them.

A-a-choo!

"I'm sorry there's no room for you too, Ted," said Farmer Dray. Ted had to walk behind, dreaming of a hot bath.

"Giddy-up, Dolly!" cried Sam.
"A-a-choo!" sneezed Ted.

Barn on
Fire

It was another busy day on Apple Tree Farm.
Poppy and Sam were helping Ted to fix a broken
fence around the sheep's field.

"Look at Woolly," said Sam. "She's not happy. She won't be able to run away on her adventures when the fence is fixed!"

Sam sniffed. There was something in the air. "Ted," he began. "What's that smell?"

Ted paused for a moment and sniffed too. "That's strange," he said. "It smells like smoke... as if something is burning."

"Look over there!" Poppy burst out.
"The barn's on fire!"

Oh no!

"It is!" said Sam. "Ted, what do we do?"
"Keep calm," Ted said. "We must run home
as fast as we can."

Ted dropped his mallet and tore across the field. Poppy grabbed Sam and they followed, running as fast as they could.

"Call for a fire truck," Ted panted.

I'll go to the barn.

Back at the farmhouse, Sam and Poppy burst through the door and everyone shouted at once.

"Call a fire truck," shouted Poppy.
"Hurry! Hurry!" shouted Sam.

Mrs. Boot called the emergency number and asked for the fire station. "Hello?" she said.

"Our barn is on fire. Please come quickly."

Soon they heard a loud siren.

"Poppy, you and Sam must stay here," said Mrs. Boot.

"Keep Rusty with you," she added. "And don't come out until I say."

Poppy, Sam and Rusty watched a gleaming
red fire truck roar into the yard.

"The fire is at the hay barn," Mrs. Boot told
them. "It's straight ahead, by the pond."

The fire truck pulled up by the barn and five firefighters jumped out. Then they unfurled the hoses and started pumping water from the pond.

"Please hurry," said Mrs. Boot. "The smoke is getting thicker."

Ted ran up with a pail full of water.
It sloshed everywhere. "Please save
the barn," he gasped.

Poppy and Sam watched from the window
as jets of water squirted over the barn.

That should put
the fire out.

"But the barn's still burning," said Sam.
"Why hasn't the smoke stopped?"

Poppy didn't know. It was very odd. Outside,
the chief firefighter thought it was odd, too.

He sent one of the firefighters to
check behind the barn.

"You won't believe this!" the firefighter called
to the others. "The barn isn't on fire at all."

Two soggy hikers had built a big camp fire and were trying to fry some sausages. More water poured over the barn, drenching them.

At last, the fire spluttered and went out. Mrs. Boot called Poppy and Sam to see what had caused all the fuss.

"We're so sorry," said the hikers. "We didn't mean to give you such a fright."

"Your sausages look very wet," said Sam.

"Never mind. Someone is enjoying them,"
said Mrs. Boot, and everyone laughed.

The Snow Storm

When Poppy and Sam looked outside, one crisp
December morning, they saw a world of white.

There had been a storm overnight and Apple Tree Farm was covered in a blanket of snow.

Poppy and Sam couldn't wait to get outside and play.

"Hats and scarves first," said Mrs. Boot, firmly.

Keep warm.

"Look at my snowman!" Poppy called, as Ted went past, dragging a sled full of hay.

"It's great, Poppy," Ted said. "But I can't stop. I need to get this to the sheep. Can you help me?"

Poppy and Sam took hold of the rope and hauled the sled over the snow.

"Oof!" panted Sam. "This is hard work."

"You're doing a grand job," said Ted.

They reached the field and looked around.
The field seemed empty.

"Where are all the sheep?" asked Poppy.

"Oh no, they're covered in snow!" cried Ted.
He rushed into the field and started brushing
snow from one of the sheep.

Poppy helped to brush the snow from the sheep, while Sam brought them fresh hay from the sled.

You poor things!

When all the sheep were clear of snow,
Poppy counted them. "One's missing!" she said.
"Where's Woolly?"

"Woolly's always running away," said Sam.
"She's such a naughty sheep."

They looked all around the snowy field, but there was no sign of Woolly anywhere.

Where can she be?

"Woof!" barked Rusty, suddenly, and bounded over the snow towards the hedge.

Woof!

"Rusty's found something," shouted Sam.
"Everyone follow Rusty!"

Ted looked under the hedge... and there was Woolly. "What are you doing in there, old girl?" he asked.

"It's too cold for hide-and-seek today, Woolly," said Sam.

"Come on, Woolly, let's get you out," said Ted, putting his arms around her and carefully pulling her from the hedge.

"Well done, Rusty," said Poppy, giving him a pat on the head. "You're a very clever dog!"

Ted and Poppy brushed the snow from Woolly.
"Time to go home," said Ted.
"WAIT!" shouted Sam. "I can see something."

Ted looked again and saw a tiny lamb. "Hello, little one," he said. "You must be frozen."

Ted gently lifted the lamb out from the hedge. "Say hello to Woolly's baby," he said.

Poppy sat on the sled, cuddling the baby lamb
in her arms. "You'll be warm soon," she whispered.

"My turn to pull the sled," said Ted. "Let's get Woolly and her new baby to the barn and out of this cold. And then it's hot drinks all round."

Tractor in Trouble

The snow lay thick on the ground at Apple Tree Farm and the wind was shaking the bare trees.

It was hard to cycle on the snow, so Poppy and Sam decided to play in the barn.

A tractor rumbled past. Poppy and Sam stopped playing to wave as it chugged by. "Hello, Ted!" they called.

"Hello you two!" he replied. "I'm off to fix the roof of the sheep shed. The wind has blown a hole in it!"

Ted propped his ladder against the shed, and carefully climbed onto the roof. The wind howled around him, getting stronger and stronger.

"Brrr! The sooner I'm back on the ground, the better," thought Ted.

At the barn, Poppy and Sam heard a terrible

CRASH!

A tree had blown over in the wind and landed
— smack — on top of Ted's tractor.

Ted was looking at his tractor in shock.

"My poor tractor," he sighed. "Look at it —
all scratched. I've only had it a week."

The tractor was trapped under the tree.

"What are you going to do?" asked Poppy.

"We'll need Farmer Dray to help us," Ted said. "He's up on the hill over there."

"We'll go and get him for you," said Poppy. She and Sam crunched through the snow as fast as they could.

Farmer Dray knew exactly what to do.
He arrived carrying a chainsaw and leading Dolly.

"Don't worry, Ted," said Farmer Dray.
"We'll soon get this sorted."

"First, I need to cut up the tree." Farmer Dray put on his goggles and the chainsaw buzzed into action. "Stand back!" he warned.

In a few minutes, the tree was a pile of logs and branches. Farmer Dray tied ropes to Dolly's harness.

He tied the other end of the ropes to the biggest, heaviest log, and Dolly began to haul it away.

"Easy does it," said Farmer Dray.

At last, the log was clear of the tractor.
"Well done, Dolly!" cried Ted.
"Hurray!" Poppy and Sam cheered.

Ted climbed back into his tractor. "Thank you, Farmer Dray and Dolly," he called. "I'd be stuck here if it wasn't for you!"

The next day, Poppy and Sam watched Ted paint his tractor.

"It will look as good as new," said Poppy.

You missed a scratch!

Ted started to polish the tractor, but the wind was picking up again. A gust whistled around the barn. It bent the trees and blew Ted's hat from his head.

"This is hopeless," Ted said. "It's far too windy to work outside today. Let's all go to the farmhouse for some hot chocolate instead."

"Yes please," said Poppy and Sam.

So they did.

Cover illustration by Simon Taylor-Kielty
Edited by Sam Taplin
Designed by Karen Tomlins, Kate Rimmer,
Krysia Ellis, Marc Maynard and Reuben Barrance
Digital manipulation: Keith Furnival

First published in 2019 by Usborne Publishing Ltd.,
Usborne House, 83-85 Saffron Hill, London EC1N 8RT, England.
www.usborne.com Copyright © 2019, 2016, 2015, 1989-1996 Usborne Publishing Ltd.

208

Camping

Ted's house

Apple Tree Farm

Apple Tree Brook

Old Mill